The Evil Doctor Mucus Spleen and Other Superbad Villains

Paul Cookson is not a villain, although he did once wait for a tortoise to reach the end of the garden and then turn it round.

He spends most of his time visiting schools, where he performs his poetry and helps pupils and staff to write their own poems. He also edits numerous poetry anthologies and performs regularly at festivals and libraries.

His favourite superhero is Batman (Adam West) and his favourite villain is Catwoman (Lee Meriwether) from the 1960s TV series – both looked good in tight-fitting suits.

Paul is married to Sally and lives in Retford with Sam, Daisy and Lightning the guinea pig.

David Parkins is deeply villainous. He has one wife, six cats, three children (one of whom he forces to play the violin) and sings very loudly to annoy the neighbours. He spends most of his time drawing pictures.

And he has a beard! Ha Ha Ha Ha HAAAAH!

The Evil Doctor Mucus Spleen

and Other Superbad Villains

Poems chosen by Paul Cookson

Illustrated by David Parkins

MACMILLAN CHILDREN'S BOOKS

Dedicated to the staff and pupils of the following primary schools: Bottesford, Croxton Kerrial, Harby, Hose, Long Clawson, Redmile, Stathern and Waltham – who all made the Vale of Belvoir Writing Project such good fun. Thanks!

First published 2001
by Macmillan Children's Books
a division of Pan Macmillan Limited
20 New Wharf Road, London N1 9RR
Basingstoke and Oxford
www.panmacmillan.com

Associated companies throughout the world

ISBN 0 330 397176

1 3 5 7 9 8 6 4 2

A CIP catalogue record for this book is available from the British Library.

Printed by Mackays of Chatham plc, Chatham, Kent.

'The Mad Magician' by John Foster first published in *Four O'Clock Friday*
by Oxford University Press 1991
'The Sound Collector' by Roger McGough first published in *Pillow Talk* (Viking),
reprinted by permission of PDF on behalf of: Roger McGough © Roger McGough

Contents

Cereal Killer

He marmalizes sugar puffs
He stabs his shredded wheat
He smothers his poor rice crispies
Yet none does Gnasher eat

He bashes up his porridge oats
Shouting, 'Death to polyfilla'
He always strikes at breakfast time
Does 'Gnash' the Cereal Killer.

Richard Caley

Villain of the Week

Monday's villain is foul of face,
Tuesday's villain has just eaten Grace,
Wednesday's villain gives loads of woe,
Thursday's villain brings ice and snow,
Friday's villain is creepy and scary,
Saturday's villain is smelly and hairy,
but the villain that's spawned on a Sunday morning,
does really nasty things – *without warning*!

Mike Johnson

Lex Loosener

When Lex Loosener leaps into town
His powers amaze and astound
He can make buttons melt
He will loosen your belt
And your trousers will fall to the ground.

Roger Stevens

Mother Christmas's Demand

Hear this, children of the world,
Father Christmas has cracked.
He's gone stark raving bonkers
and he won't be coming back.

And so, little kiddies, listen up,
from now on – you've got me.
That means NO MORE PRESENTS
under the Christmas tree.

I'm not driving that stupid sleigh
or jingling boring bells.
And you won't catch me squashing down chimneys,
or feeding reindeers. Anyway, they smell.

From now on – YOU MUST GIVE PRESENTS TO ME
Anyone who doesn't will die.
So don't be silly twits
or you'll get chopped into little bits
and baked into my next batch of mince pies.

P.S. All presents to be sent to: Mother Christmas,
Santa's Hut, Lapland.

Andrea Shavick

The Teddy Bear Terrorists

We've got your best teddy,
if you want him back,
just put everything we demand
in a sack:
either we hear by Friday
or it's tough on Ted;
you'll get him back, slowly,
we'll start with the head.

Mike Johnson

The Secret of a Super Villain

He's a shirt-blowing
all-knowing
earth-quaking
nerve-shaking
cool-kissing
near-missing
fast-talking
never-walking
supersonic
near-bionic
spine-chilling
super villain!

But only before 8 o'clock as he's afraid of the dark.
After which he becomes a:

shirt-shrinking
cocoa-drinking
mummy-kissing
teddy-missing
thumb-sucking
problem-ducking
knee-knocking
baby-rocking
subsonic
near-chronic
unwilling
chicken villain.

Andrew Collett

The Evil Doctor Mucus Spleen

Who schemes an evil scheming scheme?
Who dreams an evil dreaming dream?
Who wants to rule the world supreme?
Who has the evillest inventions?
Who has the evillest intentions?
Thoughts and plans too dark to mention . . .
The Evil Evil Evil . . . Doctor Mucus Spleen!

Who's the crime at every scene?
Who wants to turn the whole world green?
Who's not ozone friendly-clean?
His phaser laser quasar blaster
Blasts his poison ever faster
Emerald phlegm in quick-dry plaster
The Evil Evil Evil . . . Doctor Mucus Spleen!

Whose operations and routines
Take science to the dark extremes?
Who's part alien, part machine?
His cauldrons bubble, test tubes fizz.
Sockets hum and wires whizz
I bet you know just who it is . . .
The Evil Evil Evil . . . Doctor Mucus Spleen!

Whose habits are the most obscene?
Whose toes are full of jam between?
Whose armpits boil and trousers steam?
Who drips slime and goo and ooze?
Who smells of ancient sweat-stained shoes?
Who's the baddest of bad news?
The Evil Evil Evil . . . Doctor Mucus Spleen!

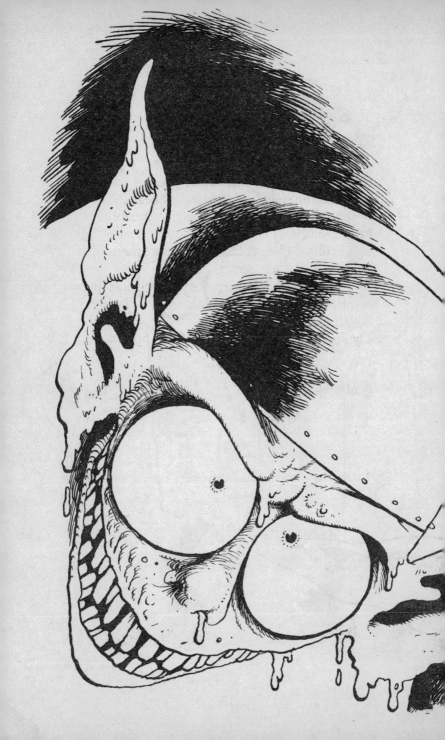

Whose underpants are trampolines?
Whose eyes are like two tangerines?
Whose skin's like rotten clotted cream?
Who has the stench of used baked beans?
Who makes your eyes and nostrils stream?
Who needs total quarantine?
The Evil Evil Evil . . . Doctor Mucus Spleen!

He's mean! He's green! He'll make you scream!
The baddest villain ever seen!
Watch out for his laser beam!
The Evil Evil Evil . . . Doctor Mucus Spleen!

Paul Cookson

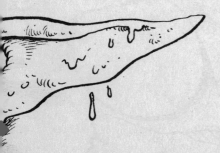

15

Last Friday Near the Shed

I was digging and I found a box.
I opened it and I found
an old red cape
a torn red mask
some mouldy red underpants
and a gun that shot red sauce.

So it was true.
My grandad really was
THE TOMATO.

All those years when he told us stories
about holding up the bus
and making all the passengers get off
just so that he could spray them with red sauce
he was telling the truth.

Imagine that.
My Grandad: THE TOMATO.

So I wonder if my grandma
really was
SQUID GIRL?

I'll get my spade.

Ian McMillan

The Sound Collector

A stranger called this morning
Dressed all in black and grey
Put every sound into a bag
And carried them away

The whistling of the kettle
The turning of the lock
The purring of the kitten
The ticking of the clock

The popping of the toaster
The crunching of the flakes
When you spread the marmalade
The scraping noise it makes

The hissing of the frying pan
The ticking of the grill
The bubbling of the bathtub
As it starts to fill

The drumming of the rain drops
On the window-pane
When you do the washing-up
The gurgle of the drain

The crying of the baby
The squeaking of the chair
The swishing of the curtain
The creaking of the stair

A stranger called this morning
He didn't leave his name
Left us only silence
Life will never be the same.

Roger McGough

The Wedding of Salmonella Toxin and Fungus Blight

It was a super villain's wedding. All the super villains came
(heroes not invited) the bride (her charming name
was Salmonella Toxin) wore a dress of poisonous green.
Among the super villains the undisputed queen,
she was marrying her sweetheart the revolting Fungus Blight,
that phosphorescent villain who glows biliously at night.
The bridesmaids were selected from the local women's jail.
All were tough and hairy and all were out on bail.
They carried little posies and their knuckledusters shone
and a hippo could have fitted in the dresses they had on.

The best man wore his costume, his notorious Ratman suit
and the presents piled up nicely, mostly bulging bags of loot.
Henchmen were the ushers and they cringed, with slimy grins
ushering the evil crowds of super villains in.
The couple were soon married. They both vowed eternal
    fights
but Salmonella promised not to poison Fungus Blight.
An arch of super death rays was the Mad Professors' treat
and the pair emerged beneath them to the sharp, staccato
    beat
of machine guns fired above them. As the bullets tinkled
    down,
"They might have used confetti!" said the bridegroom with a
    frown.

The wedding feast was sumptuous set out by the blushing
    bride
and did awful things to super villains' sensitive insides.
Then Fungus spread some mould spores as the villains
    writhed and groaned.
"We've been set up." Thin Konrad the Kleptomaniac moaned.
The happy couple made their getaway in style
knowing that their super chums were harmless for a while.
"Now the world is ours to dominate," said wily Salmonella
and snuggled up to Fungus Blight, her super villain fella.

Marian Swinger

Letter from a Super Villain's Mum

Dear World

I'm sorry that Walter (better known to you as *THE DARK LORD OF BLACKNESS, DESTROYER OF PURITY AND GOODNESS*) will not be able to rule you today as he is not feeling very well.

He has a runny nose and a temperature and is in bed with Teddy and a hot water bottle. (I did tell him to keep his vest on but does he ever take notice of his mum?!)

He has a sore throat . . . (too much evil laughing and sneering if you ask me).

The doctor says his asthma attacks may be due to an allergy to his giant white poodle *Titan* and has given him some tablets, which should help his wheezing.

With a bit of luck he should be back to making your life a misery next week – his tummy upset should have cleared up by then . . . (the toilet seat hasn't had a chance to get cold he's been on it that much . . .)

Anyway, if you could just pretend to be unhappy and downtrodden until Walter, sorry *THE DARK LORD OF BLACKNESS, DESTROYER OF PURITY AND GOODNESS* gets better that would be nice.

Yours faithfully,

Doreen Smith (Mrs)

Alias *CRUELLA MEDUSA GLOOM, MOTHER OF TERMINAL DOOM*

p.s. Meanwhile, step out of line and you'll have me to deal with!

Paul Cookson

Roll of Dishonour

Angry Alfred, the Assassin – axe, acid and 'andsaw artiste
Bold Brian, Birdbrain of the Bog, bully, braggart and beast

Charming Charlie who cheerfully chains up his chums in a
    cellar
Dirty Dora the dangerous dung-dumping dungeon dweller

Evil Eddie the egg-eating Educated Exterminator
Fat Francis the Flatulent, feared from Frankfurt to Fez and
    further

Ghastly Gertrude, the grim garrotting gran
Hideous Henry, the horrid hooded hang-gliding highwayman

Insolent Ian the Impatient Impaler who adds insult to injury
Gemstone Jeremy, jewel-thief and jester to the duped Duke of
   Germany

Comical Ken the Crooked Circus Killer – a song, a dance, a
   stab in the back
Loathsome Lady LardLips who looks like a lump of lead in a
   sack

Mad Malkie, manic mass-murderer from the Mongolian
  mafia
Nail-Up-the-Nose Norman, not no-one nastia

Oily Oliver of Aughton, awful oozing owl-disemboweller
Pongy Peter the particularly unpleasant pirate, pigfarmer and
  fowler

Queen Queechy the Quarrelsome, as queasy as an earthquake
Rude Randolf the Wretched, Rotten Robber of rubbish and
  ratcake

Simon the Slippery, second son of Septimus the Savage and
    Sarah the SlySoandSo
Twitchy Thomas the Tired Thief of Thurso

Ugly Ulric the Undertaker, he's got a living to urn
Vengeful Violent Vera the Vurst Villains' Villian

Windy Walter the Warty, waif-whacker and wobbly blob
Xerxes the extremely expert executioner and excitable slob
Yucky Yolanda the Yabbering Yob
and at the very end
Zog the Zend.

Dave Calder

Ransom Note

I'm keeping Widow Twankey
Nice and cosy in a sack –
OH, YES I AM!
And if you want her back
Bring Aladdin's old lamp
(Inclusive of genie)
To the stage door at half past four.
Signed: The Panto Meanie

Sue Cowling

Dr Dastardly Doom and the Modish Mirror

Know, O Disciple of Doom, that villains are not as vain
as the glitter-suited Goodies who spoil our fun
and so I have invented this most interesting glass
which can be fitted in shop-windows, phone-boxes –
wherever a satin spangly superhero may appear
and need to quickly check his costume is correct.
One sideways glance will be enough to turn them into
victims of fashion –
their shiny swimsuits will sprout frills,
their tights will wrinkle and sag, their feet
will wobble on suddenly stacked heels and platform soles –

The fools will stare at it like this and . . .
Aargh!!

Dave Calder

A Bad Report

Alibiology: Unbelievable

Mafimatics: Relatively poor

Meglamanery: Lacks ambition

Catastrophics: Disastrous

Plottery: Half-baked

Robgraphy: Holds everyone up

Fiendlish: Diabolical

Schemnastics: Must add more twists

Jane Clarke

My Kind of Villain

My kind of villain
is tall and thin
with a droopy moustache
that he strokes when vexed
or when considering
what kind of bad business
to get into next.
My kind of villain
in his hooded black cloak
plots wicked deeds
in a voice that's halfway
between cackle and croak,
dreams up fantastic schemes
and fiendish machines
but never succeeds:
though ruthless and strong
he's a bit of a joke –
something always goes wrong.
Dashing but dim,
doomed never to win –
that's my kind of villain

what's yours?

Dave Calder

Professor Venom's Academy for Super Villains

Timetable for Tuesday

9 a.m.   Assembly. Songs of Hate.

9.30 a.m.   Airborne superheroes. Identification from the
              ground.
              Bring silhouette charts.

10.30 a.m.   World Domination.
              How to become a dictator in ten easy goose
              steps.

11.15 a.m.   Break
              Do not destroy your enemies in the playground.
              It makes a nasty mess and puts an extra burden
              on Mr Sludge, your caretaker.

11.30 a.m.   Perfecting the fiendish cackle. You will not
              achieve your super villain's diploma until you
              have mastered this.

12 midday   Disabling your superhero. Bring your own
              Krypton. Rare and undetectable poisons for
              which there is no known antidote will be
              supplied by the Academy.

1 p.m.	Dinner
	Any student caught slipping rare and undetectable poisons for which there is no known antidote into their neighbour's Coke will be excluded. There has been too much of this lately.

2 p.m.	Mad Science
	Do it yourself Death Rays. Kits available at any good hardware store. Make sure they are European Safety Standard approved.

3 p.m.	Football. The Art of the Foul. Don't forget the match against Dr Do-Good's School for Superheroes is coming up soon so you will want to pay particular attention to this lesson.

4 p.m.	Home time.
	Once again we implore parents not to vaporise the traffic wardens. You must expect to be booked if you park your assault vehicles on the zig zag lines outside the Academy.

Marian Swinger

The Mad Magician

In a dark and dingy dungeon
The Mad Magician dwells,
Mixing poisonous potions,
Concocting evil spells.

Into his bubbling cauldron
The Mad Magician throws
Handfuls of wriggling maggots,
The eyes of two dead crows,

The bladder of a nanny goat,
The snout of a year-old pig,
An eagle's claw, a vampire's tooth,
Hairs plucked from a judge's wig.

He waves his wicked wizard's wand.
He utters a piercing cry.
From their lairs, deep in the earth,
A thousand demons fly.

In a dark and dingy dungeon
The Mad Magician dwells,
Mixing poisonous potions,
Concocting evil spells.

John Foster

Bad Eggs

Welcome to the action committee
of the truly hard-boiled.
Our mission, as our founder said,
is to "Make a mess and create a fuss!"
His martyrdom through "the accident"
when pushed off a wall will be
forever remembered.
Others also are sadly missed owing to
mishaps with electric cookers.
A minute's silence, please,
for those who have fried.
Some less worthy members have been poached
by those sunny side up do-gooders
who are ova the moon
when conversions are made.

Have patience my cracked and addled friends
revenge will be ours.
Such a stink shall we raise
that folks will name us
"the first of the phew!"
Chickens will be made to realize
who came first.
Our beloved Humpty Dumpty
had no fear of military might
as soldiers proved useless.

We have signed a pact
with demonstrators everywhere
to stand high and be ready to hand.
Keep the faith, ovoids. When the order comes –
SCRAMBLE!

John C. Desmond

5 Villains

I know who
   pushed
   Pussy down the well.
      (ding-dong)

And who
   pushed
   Humpty off the wall
      (spitter spatter)

I know who
   tripped
   Jack coming down the hill
      (Ahhhh!)

I also know
   who shot the sparrow
   who shot Cock Robin

And who put
   five and twenty blackbirds
      in the king's pie.

But I'm not telling.

I'll just give a clue.

Retep Noxid

Henchman Wanted ...

Must have mountains of muscle and not much brain
Must have loyalty beyond the call of pain
Must have hairy tattooed knuckles that reach the floor
And a head that's flat that can smash through any door.

Must have a cheerful obedient disposition
Must volunteer for every life-threatening suicide mission
Must be able to carry all the Master's equipment, no matter
    how big and strong
Must be able to take the blame when all the plans to rule the
    world go wrong.

Must be able to fight to the death while the Master gets away
Must be able to work without sleeping twenty-four hours
    every single day.
Must be able to groom and tend to every whim of his
    favourite pet, wherever sent
Must never, ever get paid – not even a single compliment.

Must be able to wash and cook, clean, iron, run the Master's
    bath
Must not get tired of the Master's evil annoying hideous
    laugh
And finally, but by no means leastly
Must always bring the Master his milky coffee and fairy cake
    on time,

No matter how much the Master is beastly.

Paul Cookson

The Evil Genius

Don't look around,
keep your eyes on the page,
act as naturally as you can.
You just need to know, before you read on,
that you're being watched by *The Evil Genius.*

What – you've never heard of *The Evil Genius,*
that genius whose mission is to tease and frustrate
for nothing more than riches and a bit of a fiendish cackle?

Well, you know how
when you try to open a crisp packet,
how you pick and pick
and nibble and pick until, finally,
you tug *so* hard
that the whole bag suddenly rips apart
in a great explosion of crisps?
(Snigger, snigger)
Well, guess who invented the crisp packet?

And you know what happens
whenever you try to use a nut cracker?
(Snigger, snigger)
Well, guess who created the nut cracker . . .
And antiseptic cream – and sticking plasters too?

And yesterday when you tried to put up that deckchair . . .
(Snigger, snigger)
what a classic!
Do I need to tell you who invented the deckchair . . .
not to mention plaster of Paris?
(Snigger, snigger)

So who am I?
I'm *The Evil Genius*' sniggering sidekick *Clever Dick*.
And why am I telling you all this?
Because there's nothing funnier than *that* look
on a victim's face
(Snigger, snigger)
when they find out they've been set up.
(Ha Ha Ha Ha Ha Ha)

Philip Waddell

King JB

We have implanted
our subject jellybabies
with micro chips,
programming them
to rise up and march
on all town halls,
railway stations and banks.
Some will penetrate the Internet
and gum up computers.
Too long have we suffered
at the hands of humans;
brutal beheadings,
torn limb from limb
and the drawn-out torture
of being sucked to death.
Enough is enough.
Passive resistance has failed;
our cries ignored.
Time for us to throw a wobbly.
Sticky wickets, traffic jams,
glue ears, bogged downs
will pale into insignificance
before the might of our forces.
Tremble all ye of the sweet tooth!

John C. Desmond

Dr D. Rision's Shopping List

scornflakes
laughing stock cubes
sour grapes
caustic soda
scathing pads
marshmalice
acid drops
throat sweets (honey and venom)
spite bulbs (40 watt)
ginger jeer
teasebags
Taunton cider
mock turtle soup
fault and pepper
Cornish nasty
crabby paste
carp
I Can't Believe it's not Bitter!
1 packet choccy takethemickeys
baked spleens
bread (Mother's Snide)
disdain remover
scoff for dinner party
gripe water.

Sue Cowling

Principal Crook

I found whilst sorting library books,
the *I Spy Book of Master Crooks*.
One 'undercover crook' selects
the sort of jobs no one suspects,
despite his being very scary –
his teeth are metal, limbs are hairy,
his eyes are cold, expression evil,
his knuckles trail, and 'looks' primeval.
He prowls around with sneers and growls,
he's patchy stubble over jowls –
he has no neck (like a gorilla),
his breath makes a good insect killer.
He likes no one, and there's a rumour,
he's no heart or sense of humour –
And I've realized this ghastly creature
is Mr Grimm, our new headteacher!

Liz Brownlee

Vocabulary for Villains

Fiendish, fearsome, filthy,
Revolting, rancid, vicious;
Detestable, disgusting,
Malevolent, malicious.

Ghastly, grisly, gruesome,
Menacing, atrocious;
Grim, grotesque, repulsive,
Loathsome, foul, ferocious.

Hellish, diabolical,
Hateful, hideous, mean;
Odious, malodorous,
Venomous, unclean.

Wicked, evil, ugly, vile,
Callous, cruel, spiteful;
Horrific, harsh, horrendous,
Pitiless and frightful.

I've given you the adjectives;
Now it's your turn to be clever:
Go ahead, enjoy it,
Write the vilest poem ever.

Eric Finney

Sidney Splatt the Custard Pie

I'm Sidney Splatt the custard pie
I love the human race
And best of all I like to spread
Custard on its face.

There isn't time to shout, 'Look out!'
Or even, 'What was that?'
Before I hit the target
Kersplosh, kersplash, kersplat!

Gareth Owen

Stinkerman

I'm Stinkerman, yes Stinkerman
stinking like a frying pan
filled with fat that's six weeks old
rancid, rotten, filled with mould
I smell of socks soaked in cheese
of rotten cabbage, putrid peas
I pong of milk that has gone sour
this is the secret of my power
you'll gag and retch, look away
and that is when I'll spoil your day.

My sweaty armpits have no hope
of ever feeling suds of soap
green fungus drips down all my teeth
my dreadful breath's beyond belief
my feet just reek, their rich aroma
certainly will knock you over
you are not even safe in bed
my awful whiff will fill your head
and as your eyes begin to close
my ghastly stench will clog your nose.

Superman fears me more
than green kryptonite
I paralyse his nerves with smells
that make him sick all night
when Batman sniffs my odours
he has to find fresh air
Spiderman just runs away
and Robin isn't there
all those superheroes
are just a foolish sham
so just remember this
I stink, therefore, I am.

David Harmer

Mirror Man

I am the world's worst supervillain
When something goes wrong I'm to blame
And I'm always one step ahead of you
Waiting to spoil your game

I arrive in your life by the side door
With no fanfare or lap of the track
Like a cold that is merely a nuisance
Or an itch in the small of the back

I'll slowly deflate your football
Loosen the screws on your shelves
For little annoyances all add up
Though they're no big deal in themselves

I'll ensure your shoe laces always untie
And you're frequently late for the train
When at last you arrive at the seaside
The sunshine will turn into rain.

Your schoolbooks drop in a puddle
Your toast lands butter-side down
You bang your knee on the table
Your smile turns into a frown

For nothing ever goes right for you
The world is a terrible place
A black cloud is always seen over your house
A grey shadow over your face

Your friends don't invite you to parties
Cos you moan from morning to night
Listen, you whinge, it's NOT MY FAULT
That nothing ever goes right.

So, will you ever dare meet me
Face to face? Eye to eye? Well, you can
For I'm hiding in your reflection
And my name is The Mirror Man.

Roger Stevens

So, You Want to Be a Super Villain — Could You Rule the World?

Which of the following names would you choose?
a) Ian the Irritatingly Annoying One?
b) Doctor Vladimir Frankendvac, Prince of Eternal Darkness?

Which outfit will you choose?
a) A yellow bobble hat and pink tutu?
b) Black suit, black gloves, black shoes, black shades, black
    cape?

Where would your ideal hideout and base be?
a) Your mum's upstairs' spare bedroom?
b) A space-station with sub-zero temperatures, totally
    undetectable by radar?

What is your source of power?
a) Fairy cakes with fresh cream?
b) Acid gamma rays from the Dark Crystal of Vortex?

You can have any superhuman power. What will it be?
a) The rapid hands of Delia, the ability to cook really fast
    soufflés?
b) The volcanic eyes of Death, the ability to become
    radioactive?

You're going to need some villainous henchmen; will it be
a) Twitty Timothy the Twerp from Twickenham and his
    friend Neville the Nauseating Nerd from Nuneaton?
b) Cruncher and Muncher, the deadly Demon twins?

What sort of pet do you want?
a) An ever so cute and cuddly Koala bear?
b) A fire-breathing, iron-clawed, people-hating, steel-plated,
stomach-churning, scaly-tailed, city-munching cave-
dwelling dragon?

What are your demands?
a) That in future everybody must be really nice to you and
   say how much they like your new hairstyle and trendy
   jeans, and not just ignore you when you walk in the
   room.
b) To make everybody in the world your slave, especially
   teachers and dinner-ladies.

Or else?
a) You'll stamp your foot and scream, very loudly.
b) You'll unleash your acid gamma rays and your volcanic
   eyes of death on everybody in the world and make them
   all cry.

**You are surrounded by Superheroes, Batman in front of
you, Superman behind you, what do you do?**
a) Run away for your cuddly Koala bear and your mummy?
b) Zap them all with your Supercharged Nasty Ray-Gun,
   turning them all into your villainous henchmen and
   RULE THE WORLD ha ha ha ha ha ha ha ha. Tee hee.

**If you scored mainly a; you are a weedy nerd who couldn't
rule a sandpit in the Nursery school, never mind the world.**

**If you scored mainly b; you are a truly evil super villain who
one day will RULE THE WORLD ha ha ha ha ha ha ha. Tee
hee.**

David Harmer and Paul Cookson

The Invisible Villain Who Doesn't Do Anything

He's been. Again.
In this room,
In this very room.
The Invisible Villain Who Doesn't Do Anything.

The chairs. The table.
Just as they were.
The cat, just there,
asleep by the fire.

The mother. The dad.
The knitting. The telly.
He's been, I tell you.
Yes, I can smell him.

He's been. Again.
In this room.
In this very room.
The Invisible Villain Who Doesn't Do Anything.

Ian McMillan

Attack of the Mutant Mangoes — a Fruit Salad Ballad of Baddies

They are totally *bananas*
They hang out on a *bunch*
Don't *trifle* with these fruitcakes
Una-*peeling*, out to lunch.
They'll *orange* a nasty accident
And *prune* you down to size,
With hands around your *neck-tarine*
You'll end up in their pies.
They're evil, they're *extrawberry*
And rotten to the core,
No more *pudding* up with them:
This is no food fight, it's a war!

Andrew Fusek Peters

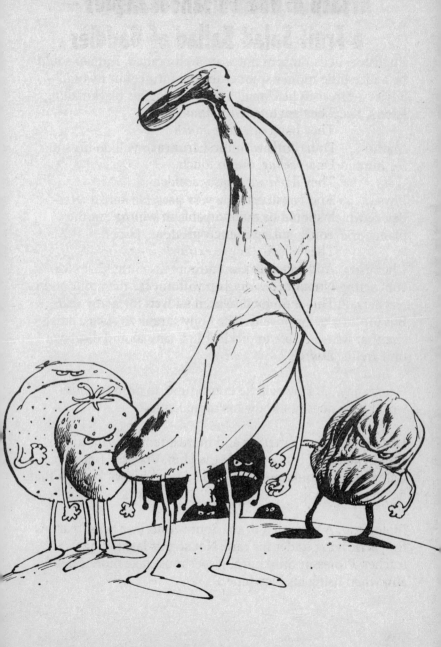

Jasper Doom's School Report

English . . . His ransom notes are well-crafted. Kidnap could be a nice little money spinner for the future, but I would advise a career in blackmail after studying his blackmailing letters. Keep up the good work, Jasper.

Maths . . . Poor, but any future henchman will do his sums for him.

Physics . . . he is constructing a very passable anti-matter device which should be quite capable of wiping out the planet or even the solar system. Well done, Jasper.

Chemistry . . . While one must admire his enthusiasm for concocting unusual poisons, he must not try them out on his teachers. Professor Slime had been with us for many years. But top marks for novelty. The body shrank to such a small size that we were able to pickle it in a jam jar and display it on Parents' Day.

Geography . . . How will he ever be able to dominate the world if he does not know his capital cities?

History . . . Less chattering and more attention paid to the super villains of history, Attila the Hun, Vlad the Impaler, Calligua, etc. would put that vital edge on his wickedness that he presently lacks.

Biology . . . A specimen of the South American poison arrow frog is thriving under his care. Not so our late biology teacher, Professor Stinkhorn. Jasper must take more careful aim when using his blowpipe.

R.E. . . . He has managed to summon two demons which is very creditable for a super brat of only eleven, however he must be prepared also to dismiss these entities. We cannot have demons being kept as pets on school premises.

Art . . . His latest sketch has caused his classmates to have recurring nightmares. Congratulations, Jasper. We are displaying it in the dining hall where it has already reduced appetites to zero.

Sport . . . There is no foul in the book that this boy has not committed. In fact, some of his fouls aren't even in the book. He has no sense of fair play at all, a vital quality in a potential super villain. He is a thoroughly bad sport and a credit to his school.

Super talents . . . He is approaching adolescence when superpowers begin to reveal themselves. He will learn to control his shape changing eventually. In the meantime we will simply lock him up when the moon is full although nothing can bring back Mr Grudge the caretaker.

Head's Comment . . . Keep up the evil work, Doom, or is it Gloom? Well done, boy. Oh, and can you give me the formula for that shrinking poison of yours? I have a feeling that my deputy head is plotting against me.

Marian Swinger

Mr Dishcloth Man's Gang —
a Bunch of Dirty Villains

Mr Dustpan had several brushes with the law
Mr Dirty Water Man saw his career go down the drain
Mr Vacuum Cleaner Man found himself on the carpet
Mr Toilet Cleaner went right round the bend

Mr Dishcloth's gang were all washed up
When
Mr Dustpan Man, who had already had several brushes with
    the law,
And Mr Washing Machine Man were caught money
    laundering
It caused Mr Dirty Water Man's career to go right down the
    drain
And sent Mr Toilet Cleaner man right round the bend.

John Coldwell

The Spider's Kiss

"I'll rule the world," said Spiderwoman
I'll send spiders through your walls
Under duvets, over pillows,
Into snoring mouths they'll crawl

Watch them go! My creeping children
Evil eyes and scuttling legs
Doing as their mother bids them
In your bedrooms and your beds

A tender kiss of deadly poison
Trickling down the silken twine
"It won't take long," said Spiderwoman.
"Planet Earth will soon be mine!"

Andrea Shavick

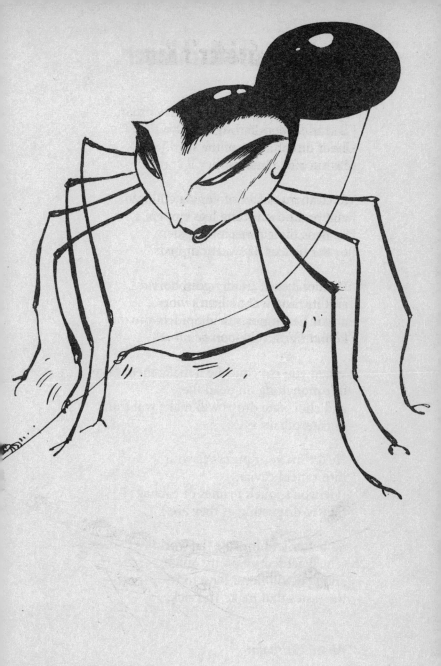

The Taste Exchanger

Beware the Taste Exchanger
and his dastardly invention –
for if he cannot rule the world
he has a vile intention

to swap the tastes of yummy things
and make them taste like kippers,
or Brussels sprouts, or bugs,
or the insides of sweaty slippers.

He'll make ice cream smell horrid
and its taste will be much worse,
and if he cannot rule the world
he'll never lift the curse.

When you eat chips he'll make them taste
like munching on dead flies,
and chocolate drops will make you think
of caterpillars' eyes.

He'll turn your pizza's flavour
into rancid caviar.
(He won't touch prunes or cabbage –
they're disgusting as they are.)

So better let him rule the world
– he'll get fed up pretty quick,
and you will never have to try
the tastes that make you sick.

Alison Chisholm

Grizelda Grimm's Ghastly Gun

I've built a giant ray-gun
and when I beam it down
nasty things will happen
to the children in your town.

I'll puncture all their footballs
ruin all their games
make sure they fight and scrap and kick
call each other names
I'll blow up their Playstations
with my wicked beam
I'll burn their burgers, zap their chocolates
melt their fresh ice-cream
my ghastly gun will trash their toys
cut their bikes in half
as their computers all explode
you'll hear my evil laugh
each time they try to chomp some gum
or chew some greasy chips
my rays will blast out super-fast
and superglue their lips
when they feel sick I'll get a kick
to watch them wail and cry
as I torch their teddies
and their CD players fry.

I think I'll start tomorrow
make my wicked dreams come true
I'm going to mess up everything
there's nothing you can do
creating stacks of chaos
is just my kind of fun
yes I'm Grizelda Grimm
with my ghoulish ghastly gun.

David Harmer

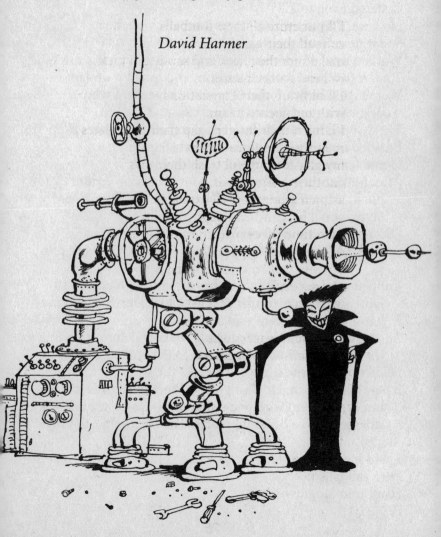

The Warthog's Diary

Wednesday August 3rd

Got up at crack of dawn to walk my giant killer dog, Fang.
Met Superman with his puny chihuahua
Ordered Fang to kill
How was I to know that it was a super chihuahua.
Spent next hour queuing up at vet's
Worked hard all morning perfecting mass hypnosis machine,
Took it to a local football stadium and tested it on fans.
Worked a treat but foiled by passing superhero who
    destroyed machine with laser vision.
These superheroes have no regard for other people's property.
Pursued by howling mob from football ground.
Home for lunch. A trough of delicious swill.
After lunch, went to library. Got out Professor Venom's latest
    book, "How To Become A Dictator In Ten Easy Goose
    Steps."
Did a bit of window shopping.
Saw a Dr Mort's Patent Death Ray half price. Couldn't resist
    it.
Jumped into Hogmobile and flew straight to Number 10
    Downing Street with Dr Mort's Patent Death Ray in my
    hand.
About to practise aim on gawking tourists before attending to
    the Prime Minister, when I was foiled once again.
Hadn't noticed the superhero across the street.
It was Elastic Man. He twanged Dr Mort's Patent Death Ray
    out of my hand with one swipe of his elastic arm. It was
    smashed into a hundred pieces. The Death Ray, not the
    arm.
I paid hard-earned loot for that Death Ray.
Pure vandalism.
Leapt into Hogmobile.

It had been wheel-clamped while my back was turned.
Went home on tube.
People kept staring at my hog bristles and my tusks.
When I become dictator, they will be the first to be enslaved.
I have noted their features.
Home. Lonely dinner of pignuts garnished with a few potato
    peelings.
Phoned girlfriend (Medusa, super villainess)
She was washing her snakes.
So, a miserable day.
I shall have to conquer the world tomorrow instead.

Marian Swinger

The Vainest Supervillain

To dandy Captain Vanity it's been clear from the start
That mighty Supervillains must strive to look the part.
That's why the Captain's shelved his plans to dominate our
    globe
Until he has decided on his villainous wardrobe.

Mini, midi, maxi, what length his flying cape?
And the CV on his chest, what style should be its shape?
And what about his colours – emerald or blue?
He likes them both but also favours red and yellow too.
And what about his underpants – the gold or silver grey?
The choice is most important since they will be on display.
And choosing stylish footwear takes time and needs great
    care
And should his hair be gelled or not or should he sport
    headgear?

And so as Captain Vanity considers – this I'll say
I hope he goes on choosing for forever and a day –
For whilst this vainest villain considers what to wear
We people on this planet *his* plans need never fear.

Philip Waddell

General Sir Pongy Cheese Feet

Cheesy the famous General
Had a weapon no one could beat
For whenever he looked like losing
He'd unsock his cheesy feet.

From between those toes his ponginess
Drifted out on the summer air
With the stink of gorgonzola
Bad fish, old underwear.

'No, not the feet!' his foes would cry
Falling to the ground
While the skies turned green and yellow
For thirty miles around.

No living thing could stand the smell
As it drifted on the breeze
Even the birds stopped singing
And fell cross-eyed from the trees.

Brave men cried out for mercy
Mothers slammed their doors
Alsatians covered their noses
With desperate, quivering paws.

But then one day the wind turned round
And before he could cry *Retreat*
Poor Cheesy fell, his nostrils filled
With the bitter smell of defeat.

Gareth Owen

Oooh-Arrrgh-Ha-Ha-Hah!

Oooh-aaarrrgh-ha-ha-hah!
That's my evil laugh;
It sounds best when it echoes
So I practise in the bath.

Oooh-aaarrrgh-ha-ha-hah!
There I go again;
I sometimes even scare myself
Every now and then.

Oooh-aaarrrgh-ha-ha-hah!
Why don't you join in?
Bare your teeth and squint your eyes,
Now, with an evil GRIN:

OOOH-AAARRRGH-HA-HA-HAH!
What a wicked din!

Celia Warren

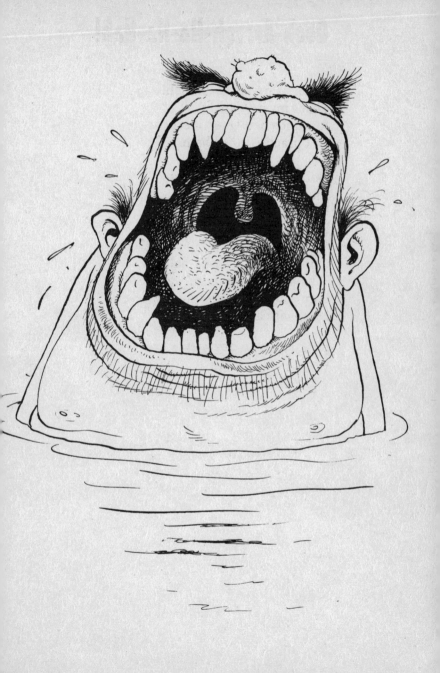

Superheroes

Fearless poems chosen by Paul Cookson

SITUATION VACANT

COULD YOU BE

our next trainee Superhero/heroine?

Immediate vacancy exists for this challenging post
With excitement and adventure guaranteed uppermost.
Your duty will be to save the planet Earth
From an evil and imminent alien invasion.
Starting salary by negotiation.
Expected age range from twenty through to forty.
Applicants should be fit and keen and sporty.
Ability to fly (without wings) even better.

    Apply now, by letter,
    With full details and C.V.
      To:—
    Save the World plc.
    P.O. Box 303
    Gotham City
    USA

(Closing date for applications is the 31st May)

Alan Priestley

A selected list of poetry books available from Macmillan

The prices shown below are correct at the time of going to press. However, Macmillan Publishers reserve the right to show new retail prices on covers which may differ from those previously advertised.

All Macmillan titles can be ordered at your local bookshop or are available by post from:

Book Service by Post
PO Box 29, Douglas, Isle of Man IM99 1BQ

Credit cards accepted. For details:
Telephone: 01624 675137
Fax: 01624 670923
E-mail: bookshop@enterprise.net

Free postage and packing in the UK.
Overseas customers: add £1 per book (paperback)
and £3 per book (hardback).